PIANO · VOCAL · GUITAR

The Big Book of Love & Wedding Songs

ISBN 0-7935-1440-1

HLP Hal Leonard Publishing Corporation

7777 West Bluemound Road P.O. Box 13819 Milwaukee, WI 53213

Contents

AIR
(from Water Music Suite)

G. F. HANDEL

Slowly and stately

ALL I ASK OF YOU
(From "THE PHANTOM OF THE OPERA")

Music by ANDREW LLOYD WEBBER
Lyrics by CHARLES HART
Additional Lyrics by RICHARD STILGOE

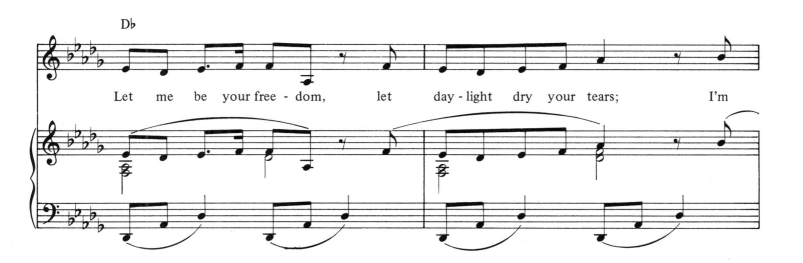

ALL MY LOVING

Words and Music by
JOHN LENNON and PAUL McCARTNEY

MCA music publishing

All the Things You Are

(From "VERY WARM FOR MAY")

Words by OSCAR HAMMERSTEIN II
Music by JEROME KERN

Moderately Slowly

You are the prom-ised kiss of spring-time That
makes the lone-ly win-ter seem long. _____
You are the breath-less hush of eve-ning That

AND I LOVE HER

Words and Music by
JOHN LENNON and PAUL McCARTNEY

AND I LOVE YOU SO

Words and Music by
DON McLEAN

MCA music publishing

ANNIVERSARY SONG

By AL JOLSON
and SAUL CHAPLIN

Moderately Slow

AND THIS IS MY BELOVED

(From "KISMET")

Words and Music by ROBERT WRIGHT and GEORGE FORREST
(Music Based on Themes of A. BORODIN)

THE ANNIVERSARY WALTZ

Words and Music by
AL DUBIN and DAVE FRANKLIN

Moderately

CAN'T HELP FALLING IN LOVE

Words and Music by GEORGE DAVID WEISS,
HUGO PERETTI, and LUIGI CREATORE

AVE MARIA
(The melody adapted to the First Prelude of the Well-tempered Clavier of Johann Sebastian Bach)

CHARLES GOUNOD
English Text from ST. LUKE

44418

AVE MARIA

Very slowly

Music by FRANZ SCHUBERT
Traditional liturgical text

*pronounced grah - tsee - ah

na, A - ve, A - ve! Do - mi - nus Do - mi - nus _____ te - cum, Be - ne -

di - cta tu in mu - li - e - ri - bus, et be - ne - di - ctus, et

be - ne - di - ctus fru - ctus ven - tris, ven - tris, tu - i, Je - sus.**

A - ve Ma - ri - a!

** pronounced yeh - zoos

42

To Coda

ho - ra mor - tis no - strae, in ho - ra mor - tis, mor - tis no - strae, in

ho - ra mor - tis no - strae. A - ve Ma - ri -

D.S. al Coda

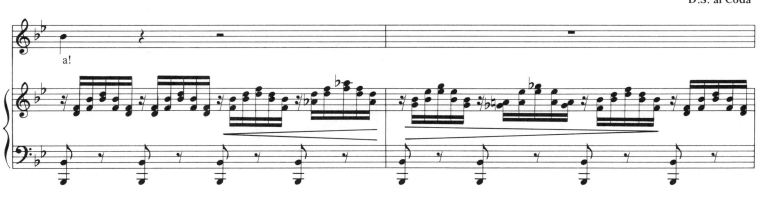

a!

CODA

dim.

BECAUSE

Words by EDWARD TESCHEMACHER
Music by GUY D' HARDELOT

BECAUSE I LOVE YOU
(The Postman Song)

Words and Music by
WARREN ALLEN BROOKS

BRIDAL CHORUS
(From "Lohengrin")

RICHARD WAGNER

(THEY LONG TO BE)
CLOSE TO YOU

Lyric by HAL DAVID
Music by BURT BACHARACH

COULD I HAVE THIS DANCE

Words and Music by WAYLAND HOLYFIELD
and BOB HOUSE

Moderately Slow

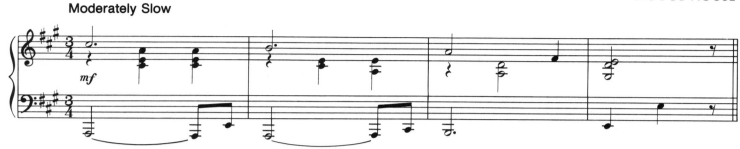

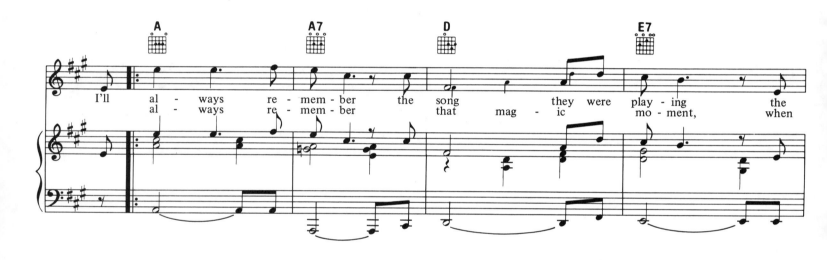

I'll al - ways re - mem - ber the song they were play - ing, the when
al - ways re - mem - ber that mag - ic mo - ment,

first time_____ we danced and I knew.
I held_____ you close to me.

As we
As

DEDICATED TO THE ONE I LOVE

Words and Music by LOWMAN PAULING
and RALPH BASS

MCA music publishing

fied _____ know-ing ____ you __ love me. ____ There's one thing I want you to

do es - pe - cial - ly for me And it's some - thing ____ that

ev - 'ry-bod - y needs. _____

D.S. al Coda I

CODA I

hard for me my ba - by, _____ And the dark - est hour __

DEVOTED TO YOU

Words and Music by BOUDLEAUX BRYANT

DON'T KNOW MUCH

Words and Music by BARRY MANN,
CYNTHIA WEIL and TOM SNOW

DREAMS TO DREAM
(Finale Version)
(From the Universal Motion Picture "AN AMERICAN TAIL: FIEVEL GOES WEST")

Words and Music by
JAMES HORNER and WILL JENNINGS

I lose my way,   no-one cares.

The words I ___ say   no-one hears.   My life, it ___ seems

your   dreams___   will   come___
will   al - ways

true.___

ENDLESS LOVE

Words and Music by
LIONEL RICHIE

EASY TO LOVE
(From "BORN TO DANCE")

Words and Music by
COLE PORTER

Moderately

You'd be so eas-y to love, So eas-y to i-dol-ize, all oth-ers a-bove, So worth the yearn-ing for,_____ So swell to keep ev'-ry home fire burn-

FEELINGS
(¿Dime?)

English Words and Music by MORRIS ALBERT
Spanish Lyric by THOMAS FUNDORA

Moderately Slow

FOR ALL WE KNOW

(From the Motion Picture "LOVERS AND OTHER STRANGERS")

Words by ROBB WILSON and JAMES GRIFFIN
Music by FRED KARLIN

Moderato, with a light beat

(I Love You)
FOR SENTIMENTAL REASONS

Words by DEEK WATSON
Music by WILLIAM BEST

FOREVER AND EVER, AMEN

Words and Music by DON SCHLITZ
and PAUL OVERSTREET

MCA music publishing

THE GIRL THAT I MARRY

Words and Music by
IRVING BERLIN

The girl that I mar-ry will have to be as soft and as

GROW OLD WITH ME

Moderate ballad

Words and Music by
JOHN LENNON

Grow old a-long with me___
old a-long with me___
Grow old a-long with me___ The
Two
What -

best is yet to be___ When our time has come___
branch - es of one tree___ Face the set - ting sun___
ev - er of fate de - crees___ We will see it through___

We will be as one___
When the day is done___
For our love is true___

God bless our love___ God bless our love___

To Coda

1. Grow

2.

THE HAWAIIAN WEDDING SONG

English Words by AL HOFFMAN and DICK MANNING
Hawaiian Words and Music by CHARLES E. KING

Slowly, with much warmth

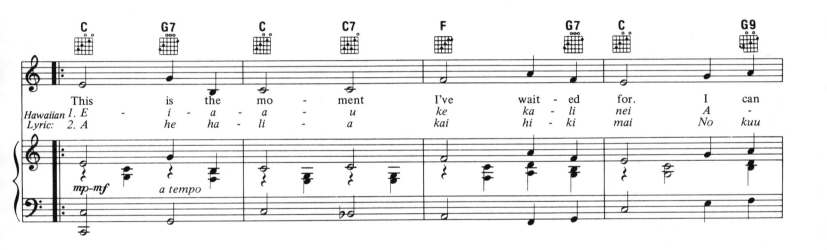

This is the mo - ment I've wait - ed for. I can

Hawaiian 1. E - i - a - a - u ke ka - li nei A No kuu
Lyric: 2. A he ha - li - a kai hi - ki mai No kuu

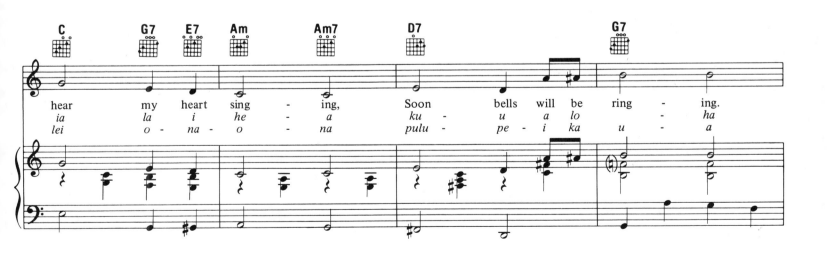

hear my heart sing - ing, Soon bells will be ring - ing.
ia la i he - a ku - u a lo - ha
lei o - na - o - na pulu - pe - i ka u - a

HERE AND NOW

Words and Music by TERRY STEELE
and DAVID ELLIOT

HOW DEEP IS YOUR LOVE

Words and Music by BARRY GIBB,
MAURICE GIBB and ROBIN GIBB

I CHOSE RIGHT

(From The Musical "BABY")

Lyrics by RICHARD MALTBY, JR.
Music by DAVID SHIRE

I LOVE YOU TRULY

I PLEDGE MY LOVE

Words by DINO FEKARIS
Music by DINO FEKARIS and FREDDIE PERREN

I'LL BE BY YOUR SIDE

Words and Music by STEVIE B.
and DADGEL ATABAY

I'LL ALWAYS LOVE YOU

Words and Music by
JIMMY GEORGE

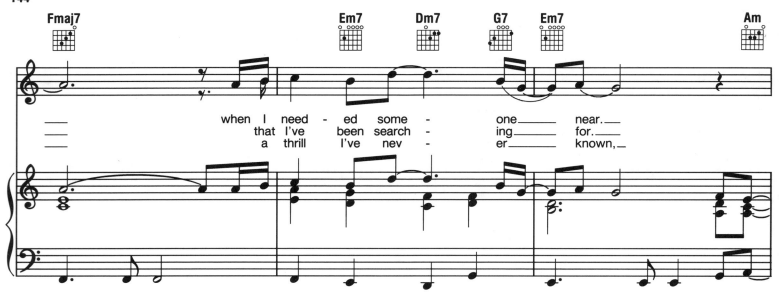

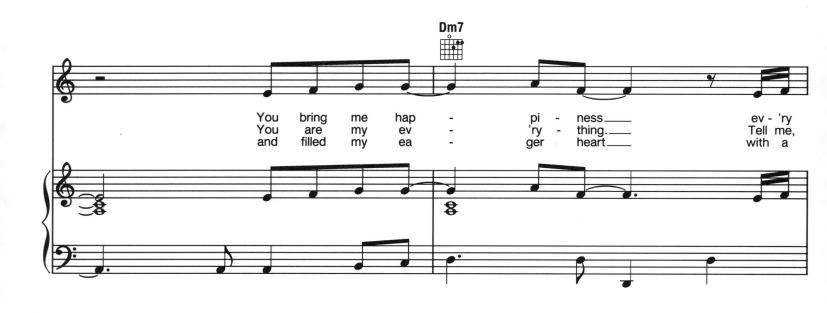

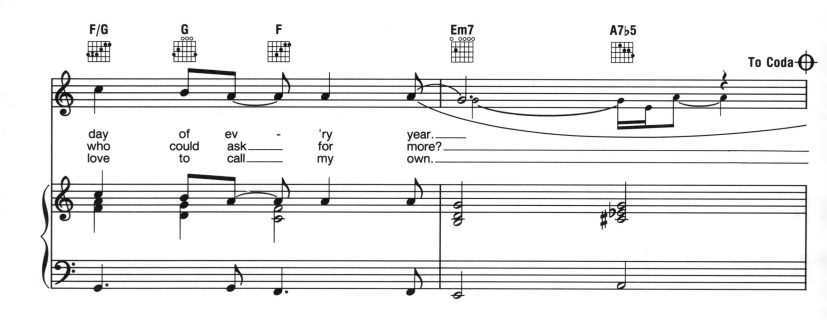

JESU, JOY OF MAN'S DESIRING

By J.S. BACH

Ho - ly wis - dom,
Hark, what peace - ful

love____ most____ bright,
mu - sic____ rings,

Drawn
Where

by the

Word of God our flesh that fash - ioned,
Theirs is beau - ty's fair - est plea - sure,

With the fire of life im - Striv - ing still to truth un -
Theirs is wis - dom's ho - liest trea - sure. Thou dost ev - er lead Thine

JUST THE WAY YOU ARE

Words and Music by
BILLY JOEL

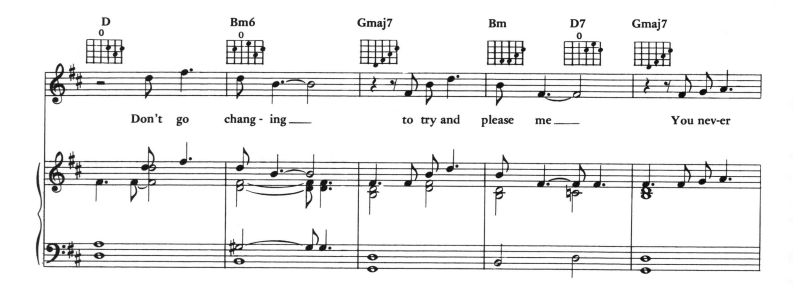

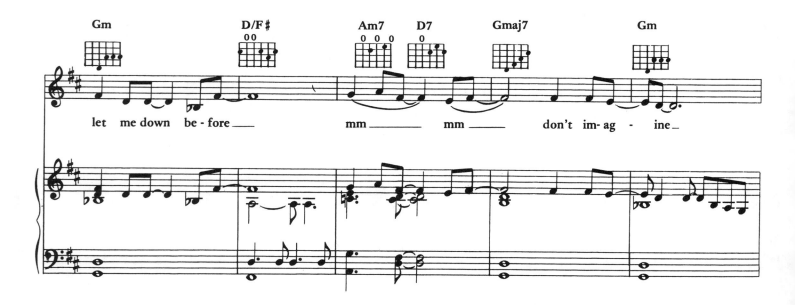

LONGER

Words and Music by
DAN FOGELBERG

Long - er than_ there've been fish - es in the o - cean,
Strong - er than_ an - y moun - tain cath - e - - dral.
Through the years_ as the fi - re starts to mel - low,

THE LAST TIME I FELT LIKE THIS
(From "SAME TIME, NEXT YEAR")

Words by ALAN BERGMAN
and MARILYN BERGMAN
Music by MARVIN HAMLISCH

Slow Ballad tempo

Hel - lo, I don't_ e - ven know_ your name, but I'm hop-in' all_ the
lo, I can't_wait till we're_ a - lone, some - where qui-et on_ our

same this is more than just a sim - ple hel - lo. Hel - lo, do I smile and walk_ a -
own so that we can fall the rest_ of the way. I know that be - fore the night_ is

way? No, I think I'll smile_ and stay to see where this might_ go.
thru, I'll be talk-ing love_ to you, mean-ing ev-'ry word I____ say.

'Cause The Last Time I Felt Like This

LOST IN YOUR EYES

Words and Music by
DEBORAH GIBSON

LOVE IS HERE TO STAY

(From "GOLDWYN FOLLIES")

Words by IRA GERSHWIN
Music by GEORGE GERSHWIN

LOVE ME TENDER

Words and Music by ELVIS PRESLEY,
and VERA MATSON

Moderately slow

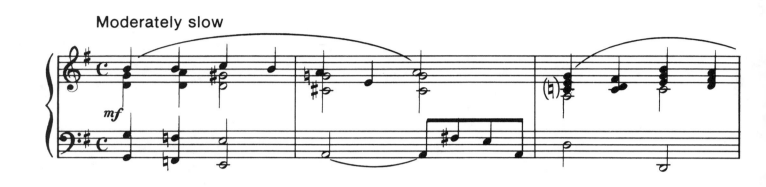

Verse

1. Love Me Ten - der, love me sweet;
2. Love Me Ten - der, love me long;
3. Love Me Ten - der, love me dear;

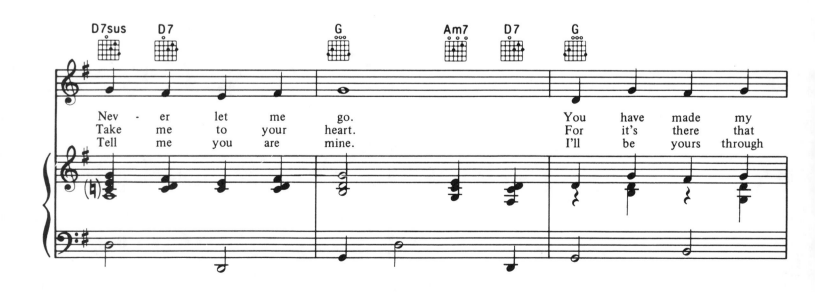

Nev - er let me go.
Take me to your heart.
Tell me you are mine.

You have made my
For it's made there that
I'll be yours through

EXTRA VERSE 4. When at last my dreams come true,
Darling, this I know:
Happiness will follow you
Everywhere you go.

LOVE OF A LIFETIME

By BILL LEVERTY and CARL SNARE

LOVING YOU

Words and Music by
MIKE STOLLER and JERRY LEIBER

Moderately slow

I will spend my whole life through lov - ing you, __ lov - ing you. __ Win - ter, sum - mer spring - time, too, lov - ing you, __ lov - ing you __ makes no dif - f'rence

LOVE WITHOUT END, AMEN

Words and Music by
AARON G. BARKER

MAY YOU ALWAYS

Words and Music by LARRY MARKES
and DICK CHARLES

MY CUP RUNNETH OVER

(From "I DO! I DO!")

Words by TOM JONES
Music by HARVEY SCHMIDT

MARRY ME

(From The Musical "THE RINK")

Lyrics by FRED EBB
Music by JOHN KANDER

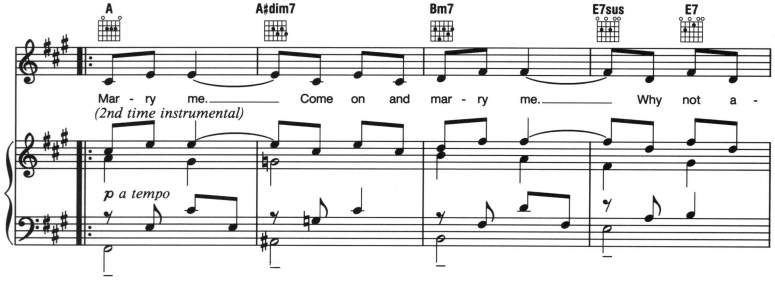

Mar-ry me. ____ Come on and mar-ry me. ____ Why not a-
(2nd time instrumental)

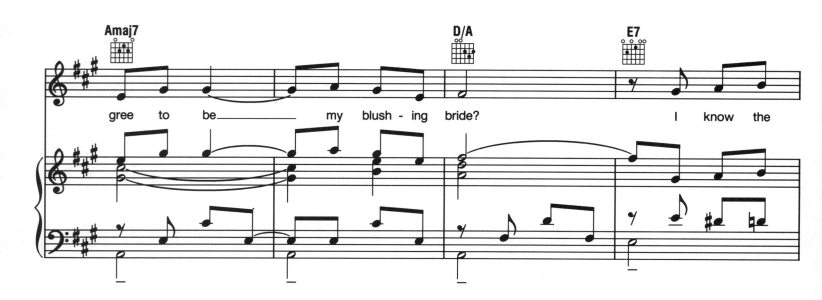

gree to be ____ my blush-ing bride? I know the

NEVERTHELESS

(I'm In Love With You)

Words and Music by
BERT KALMER and HARRY RUBY

OH, PROMISE ME!

Words by CLEMENT SCOTT
Music by REGINALD de KOVEN

PEOPLE WILL SAY WE'RE IN LOVE

(From "OKLAHOMA!")

Lyrics by OSCAR HAMMERSTEIN II
Music by RICHARD RODGERS

SO AMAZING

Words and Music by
LUTHER VANDROSS

Slowly with feeling

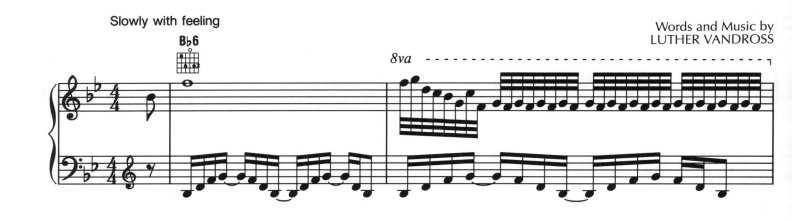

Love has truly been good to me.
Got to tell you how you thrill me.

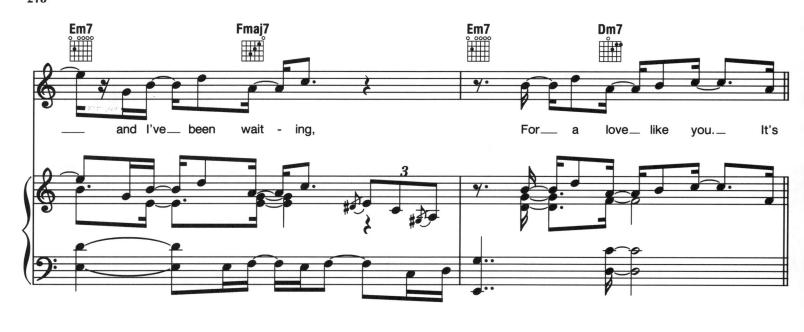

and I've— been wait - ing, For— a love— like you.— It's

so a - ma - zing to— be loved.— I'd fol - low you— to the moon and the sky a - bove.—

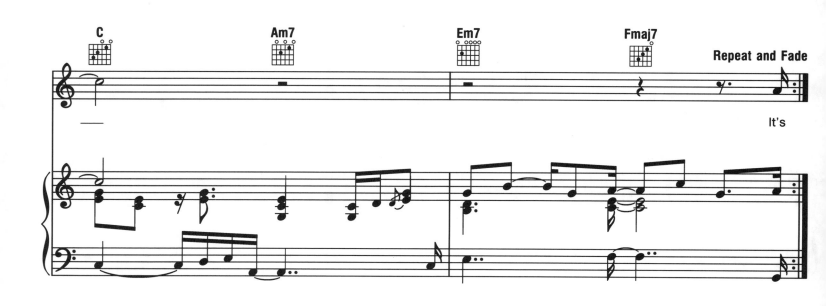

Repeat and Fade

It's

SOMETHING

Words and Music by
GEORGE HARRISON

SO IN LOVE

(From "KISS ME KATE")

Words and Music by
COLE PORTER

love   with   you,   my   love _____ am

SOMEWHERE OUT THERE
(From "AN AMERICAN TAIL")

By JAMES HORNER,
BARRY MANN and CYNTHIA WEIL

SUNRISE, SUNSET
(From "FIDDLER ON THE ROOF")

Words by SHELDON HARNICK
Music by JERRY BOCK

Moderately Slow Waltz Tempo
(soulful and wistful)

Is this the lit-tle boy I car - ried? Is this the lit-tle girl at
Now is the lit-tle boy a bride - groom, Now is the lit-tle girl a

play? I don't re - mem-ber grow - ing old - er,
bride. Un - der the can-o-py I see them,

When did they? When did she get to be a
Side by side. Place the gold ring a - round her

STRANGER IN PARADISE

(From "KISMET" and "TIMBUKTU!")

Words and Music by ROBERT WRIGHT and GEORGE FORREST
(Music Based on Themes of A. BORODIN)

THAT'S WHAT LOVE IS FOR

Words and Music by MARK MUELLER,
MICHAEL OMARTIAN and AMY GRANT

Moderate Ballad

Lyrics:

Some-times we make it harder than it is.

We'll take a per-fect night and fill it up with words we don't mean. Dark sides best un-seen. And we won-der why we're feel-ing this way.

- by that's _ what_ love _ is for._

Guitar solo - ad lib.

Solo ends

Be -

liev- ing in __ the one_____ thing_ that has got- ten us__ this far._____

THIS I PROMISE YOU

Words and Music by
CLYDE OTIS and VINCENT CORSO

THROUGH THE YEARS

Words and Music by STEVE DORFF
and MARTY PANZER

THE TIES THAT BIND

Words and Music by CLYDE OTIS and VINCENT CORSO

TILL

Words by CARL SIGMAN
Music by CHARLES DANVERS

TOGETHER

Words and Music by B.G. DESYLVA,
RAY HENDERSON and LEW BROWN

Moderately Slow

TRUE LOVE

Words and Music by
COLE PORTER

Moderately Slow

TRUMPET TUNE

JEREMIAH CLARKE

TRUMPET VOLUNTARY

JEREMIAH CLARKE

THE VOWS GO UNBROKEN
(ALWAYS TRUE TO YOU)

Words and Music by GARY BURR
and ERIC KAZ

TOO MUCH HEAVEN

Words and Music by BARRY GIBB,
MAURICE GIBB, and ROBIN GIBB

love an-y more, it's as high as a moun-tain and hard-er to climb.___

Oh, you and me, girl,___ got a lot of love in store, and it
Oh, you and me, girl,___ got a high-way to the sky, we can

flows through you and it flows through me and I love you so much more than my
turn a-way from the night and day and the tears we had to cry, you're my

life. I can see be-yond for-ev-er, ev-'ry-thing we are will nev-er
life. I can see a new to-mor-row, ev-'ry-thing we are will nev-er

WEDDING MARCH

FELIX MENDELSSOHN

WEDDING PROCESSIONAL

(From "THE SOUND OF MUSIC")

Lyrics by OSCAR HAMMERSTEIN II
Music by RICHARD RODGERS

Majestically

For the entrance of the Bride

WHAT THE WORLD NEEDS NOW IS LOVE

Lyric by HAL DAVID
Music by BURT BACHARACH

WHEN I FALL IN LOVE

Words by EDWARD HEYMAN
Music by VICTOR YOUNG

WHEN I'M WITH YOU

Words and Music by
ARNOLD DAVID LANNI

with you. When I'm with you.

WHITHER THOU GOEST

Words and Music by
GUY SINGER

Moderately slow

Chorus

Whith - er Thou Go - est I will go._____ Wher -

ev - er thou lodg - est I will lodge._____ Thy peo - ple shall

be my peo - ple, my love. Whith - er Thou Go - est I will

WITH THIS RING

Words and Music by
CLYDE OTIS and VINCENT CORSO

YOU DECORATED MY LIFE

Words and Music by
DEBBIE HUPP and BOB MORRISON

All my life was a pa-per_____ once plain, pure and white;_____
rhyme with no rea-son_____ in an un-fin-ished song;_____

Till you moved with your pen_____ chang-in' moods now and then_____ till the
There was no har-mo-ny_____ life meant noth-in' to me,_____ un-til

bal-ance was right._____ Then you add-ed some mu-sic,_____
you came a-long._____ And you brought out the col-ors,_____

YOU NEEDED ME

Words and Music by
RANDY GOODRUM

Moderately

I cried a tear,   you wiped it dry,   I was con- fused   you cleared my
hand,   when it was cold,   when I was lost   you took me

mind,   I sold my soul,   you bought it back for me __   and held me
home   You gave me hope,   when I was at the end __   and turned my

YOU'RE MY EVERYTHING

J. M. DE SCARANO, N. SKORSKY and L. GOMEZ

YOU'LL NEVER WALK ALONE
(From "CAROUSEL")

Lyrics by OSCAR HAMMERSTEIN II
Music by RICHARD RODGERS

THE
GREATEST SONGS EVER WRITTEN

Arranged for Piano, Voice & Guitar

50 OF THE MOST BEAUTIFUL SONGS EVER

Over 400 pages of slow and sentimental ballads, including: Come In From The Rain • Edelweiss • The First Time Ever I Saw Your Face • For All We Know • How Deep Is Your Love • I Have Dreamed • I'll Be Seeing You • If We Only Have Love • Love Is Blue • Red Roses For A Blue Lady • Songbird • Summertime • Unchained Melody • Yesterday, When I Was Young • Young At Heart • many more.

____00360735 ....$19.95

THE BEST LOVE SONGS EVER
Newly revised!

A collection of 66 favorite love songs, including: The Anniversary Song • (They Long To Be) Close To You • Endless Love • Here and Now • Just The Way You Are • Longer • Love Takes Time • Misty • My Funny Valentine • So In Love • You Needed Me • Your Song.

____00359198 ....$15.95

THE BEST BIG BAND SONGS EVER
Newly revised!

40 of the greatest big band songs ever, including: Ballin' The Jack • Basin Street Blues • Boogie Woogie Bugle Boy • The Continental • Don't Get Around Much Anymore • In The Mood • Let A Smile Be Your Umbrella • Marie • Moonglow • Opus One • Satin Doll • Sentimental Journey • String Of Pearls • Who's Sorry Now.

____00359129 ....$15.95

THE BEST CHRISTMAS SONGS EVER
Newly revised!

A collection of 72 of the most-loved songs of the season, including: Blue Christmas • The Chipmunk Song • Frosty The Snow Man • A Holly Jolly Christmas • Home For The Holidays • I'll Be Home For Christmas • Jingle-Bell Rock • Let It Snow! Let It Snow! Let It Snow ! • Parade Of The Wooden Soldiers • Rudolph The Red-Nosed Reindeer • Crazy Snowflake • Toyland • Up On The House-top • What Child Is This?

____00359130 ....$15.95

THE BEST ROCK SONGS EVER

70 of the best rock songs from yesterday & today, including: All Day And All Of The Night • All Shook Up • Ballroom Blitz • Bennie And The Jets • Blue Suede Shoes • Born To Be Wild • Boys Are Back In Town • Every Breath You Take • Faith • Free Bird • Hey Jude • I Still Haven't Found What I'm Looking For • Livin' On A Prayer • Lola • Louie Louie • Maggie May • Money • (She's) Some Kind Of Wonderful • Takin' Care Of Business • Walk This Way • We Didn't Start The Fire • We Got The Beat • Wild Thing • more!

____00490424 ....$14.95

THE BEST COUNTRY SONGS EVER
Newly revised!

We've updated this outstanding collection of country songs to include even more of your favorites — over 65 in all! Featuring: Always On My Mind • Behind Closed Doors • Could I Have This Dance • Crazy • Daddy Sang Bass • D-I-V-O-R-C-E • Forever And Ever, Amen • God Bless The U.S.A. • Grandpa (Tell Me 'Bout The Good Old Days) • Help Me Make It Through The Night • I Fall To Pieces • If We Make It Through December • Jambalaya (On The Bayou) • Love Without End, Amen • Mammas Don't Let Your Babies Grow Up To Be Cowboys • Stand By Your Man • Through The Years • and more.

____00359135 ....$15.95

THE BEST STANDARDS EVER
Newly Revised!
Volume 1 (A-L)

72 beautiful ballads, including: All The Things You Are • Bewitched • Can't Help Lovin' Dat Man • Don't Get Around Much Anymore • Getting To Know You • God Bless' The Child • Hello, Young Lovers • I Got It Bad And That Ain't Good • It's Only A Paper Moon • I've Got You Under My Skin • The Lady Is A Tramp • Little White Lies.

____00359231 ....$15.95

Volume 2 (M-Z)

72 songs, including: Makin' Whoopee • Misty • Moonlight In Vermont • My Funny Valentine • Old Devil Moon • The Party's Over • People Will Say We're In Love • Smoke Gets In Your Eyes • Strangers In The Night • Tuxedo Junction • Yesterday.

____00359232 ....$15.95

THE BEST EASY LISTENING SONGS EVER
Newly revised!

A collection of 75 mellow favorites, featuring: All Out Of Love • Can't Smile Without You • (They Long To Be) Close To You • Every Breath You Take • Eye In The Sky • How Am I Supposed To Live Without You • I Dreamed A Dream • Imagine • Love Takes Time • Piano Man • The Rainbow Connection • Sing • Vision Of Love • Your Song.

____00359193 ....$15.95

THE BEST SONGS EVER!
Newly revised!

This prestigious collection has just been updated and revised to include even more recent "contemporary classics" — 76 songs in all, featuring: All I Ask Of You • Cabaret • Can't Smile Without You • Candle In The Wind • Do-Re-Mi • Don't Know Much • Feelings • Fly Me To The Moon • The Girl From Ipanema • Here's That Rainy Day • I Can't Help Falling In Love • I Left My Heart In San Francisco • I Write The Songs • Imagine • In The Mood • Let it Be Me • Longer • Love On The Rocks • More • My Way • People • Send In The Clowns • Some Enchanted Evening • Somewhere Out There • Stormy Weather • Strangers In The Night • Sunrise, Sunset • What A Wonderful World.

____00359224 ....$17.95

THE BEST BROADWAY SONGS EVER
Newly revised!

We've made this book even better with the addition of songs from some of Broadway's latest blockbusters such as Phantom Of The Opera, Les Miserables, Miss Saigon, and Aspects Of Love — over 65 songs in all! Highlights include: All I Ask Of You • As Long As He Needs Me • Bess, You Is My Woman • Bewitched • Camelot • Climb Ev'ry Mountain • Comedy Tonight • Don't Cry For Me Argentina • Everything's Coming Up Roses • Getting To Know You • I Could Have Danced All Night • I Dreamed A Dream • If I Were A Rich Man • The Last Night Of The World • Love Changes Everything • Oklahoma! • Ol' Man River • People • Try To Remember • and many, many more!

____00309155 ....$15.95

HP® **Hal Leonard Publishing Corporation**
777 West Bluemound Road P.O. Box 13819 Milwaukee, WI 53213